The Gift of
Haley

Terri Bené and Rosemary Lyn
Illustrations by Marty Petersen

The Gift of Haley
by Terri Bené and Rosemary Lyn

Published by

TheDot Press

haleysworldbooks.com

Illustrations: Marty Petersen, www.martyart.com
Book Layout: Nick Zelinger, NZ Graphics, www.nzgraphics.com

ISBN 978-1-947444-00-3 (Hard cover)
ISBN 978-1-947444-02-7 (Soft cover)
ISBN 978-1-947444-01-0 (eBook)

LCCN: 2017910915

Printed in the United States of America

First Edition

This book belongs to
Haley's friend

It took Emily forever to make
the perfect Valentine's heart
for the boy next door...

...and only a moment for him to break it!

Emily vowed she would never give her heart away again.

Hoping to cheer her up, Emily's parents gave her a special Valentine's Day gift.

But one look at Haley and
Emily knew she could not
be trusted.

It took no time at all for
Emily's fears to come true.
Haley was a thief!

Emily came up with a plan
to train Haley.

But that night, her glasses were not in the right spot.

And the next day, Emily's mother missed her doctor's appointment searching for a matching pair of shoes.

Emily was shocked on Easter
morning when no eggs...or
even flowers...could be found
in the garden.

From that moment on, Emily knew she would have to be on guard.

At the softball game, Emily
was out when home base
was already stolen.

And Emily's mother needed
a ride to work because her
car keys were missing.

Emily's father was upset that
he lost the round of golf when
his favorite club vanished.

22

By the 4th of July, Emily decided she would have to keep a closer eye on Haley.

But nobody slept the night
Emily's baby brother lost
his stuffed lion.

There were more tricks than treats when someone ate all the Halloween candy.

Emily's mother had no idea
what happened to the
pumpkin pie she baked
for Thanksgiving.

Emily vowed to stay with Haley day and night.

But Emily's family missed
their favorite Christmas
show searching everywhere
for the lost remote.

And bath time did not go
well without the baby's
rubber duck.

Finally, when Emily's mother could not find her pearl necklace for the New Year's Eve party...

...Emily GAVE IN!

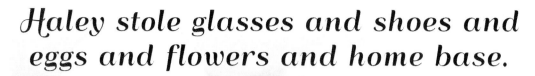

Haley stole glasses and shoes and eggs and flowers and home base.

She stole keys and golf clubs and a stuffed lion and candy.

She stole pie and the remote and a rubber duck and a pearl necklace.

But on the very next
Valentine's Day...

...Emily gave Haley her heart.

About the Authors and Illustrator

Along with her siblings, Jake & Gracie, Haley was born January 4, 2003, and Haley and Jake became Rosemary Lyn's dog-children on Valentine's Day. Haley is sweet, loving, and energetic ... and she is a thief! Her preference is for shiny objects. Haley brought three friends together to tell her story:

Terri Bené is a children's book author, as well as the mother of seven and grandmother of six (so far!). She has shared a log home in the beautiful Colorado Rockies with her family and many furry creatures for over 30 years. After recently completing a degree in psychology, she is now thinking about what she wants to be when she grows up.

Rosemary Lyn was born June 22, 1965, in Lakewood, California to the most loving mother on earth, Rosemary Senior. She is a software engineer by education and has lived in sunny Arizona for 25 years. Her real job is being a "dog mom" to Haley and Jake. She is committed to all children learning and laughing.

Marty Petersen grew up drawing, painting, sculpting and carving anything he could get his hands on. After receiving degrees in Illustration and Commercial Art from Kendall School of Design in Michigan, Marty relocated to Colorado where he has worked as a designer, illustrator, and wood carver for several years. Best known as the artist who illustrated the "Justification for Higher Education" poster, his first love is illustrating children's books. Marty's website is ***martyart.com.***

Follow Haley and her lovable adventures at ***haleysworldbooks.com.***

We'd love to hear from you!

Connect with us at **haleysworldbooks** on

Facebook	Twitter	Instagram	Pinterest